summer 2003

All I Have	Jennifer Lopez	2
American Life	Madonna	9
Can't Nobody	Kelly Rowland	20
Come Undone	Robbie Williams	26
Couldn't Have Said It Better	Meat Loaf	32
Crazy In Love	Beyoncé	41
Here It Comes Again	Mel C	50
I Begin To Wonder	Dannii Minogue	57
I Can't Break Down	Sinead Quinn	62
If I Fall	Aqualung	76
I'm With You	Avril Lavigne	80
Incredible (What I Meant To Say)	Darius	69
Keep Me A Secret	Ainslie Henderson	86
Lost Without You	Delta Goodrem	92
Love Doesn't Have To Hurt	Atomic Kitten	98
Make Me Smile (Come Up And See Me)	Erasure	104
Midnight	Uncut	108
No Good Advice	Girls Aloud	112
Not Gonna Get Us	t.A.T.u.	118
On The Horizon	Mel C	130
Out Of Time	Blur	136
Rock Your Body	Justin Timberlake	140
Say Goodbye	S Club	125
Spirit In The Sky	Gareth Gates	148
Sunday (The Day Before My Birthday)	Moby	153
Sunrise	Simply Red	160
Thinking About Tomorrow	Beth Orton	164
To Love A Woman	Lionel Richie/Enrique Iglesias	168
Wimmin	Ashley Hamilton	176
You Said No	Busted	181

Published 2003

Editorial and new arrangements and engraving by Artemis Music Limited
Cover Design: Space DPS Limited

International MUSIC Publications

© International Music Publications Limited
Griffin House 161 Hammersmith Road London W6 8BS England

All I Have

words and music by
**Jennifer Lopez, Makeba Riddick, Ronald Bowser,
Curtis Richardson, William Jeffrey and
Lisa Peters**

highest chart position **2**
release date **10th March 2003**

did you know J-Lo's single features a scene-stealing contribution from LL Cool J, the one-time platinum-selling boy prodigy who is fast approaching middle age.

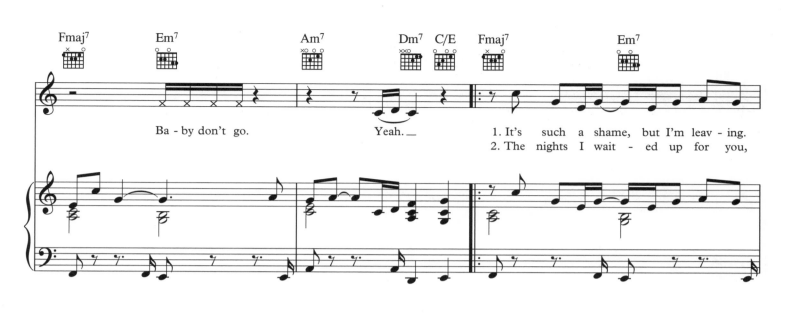

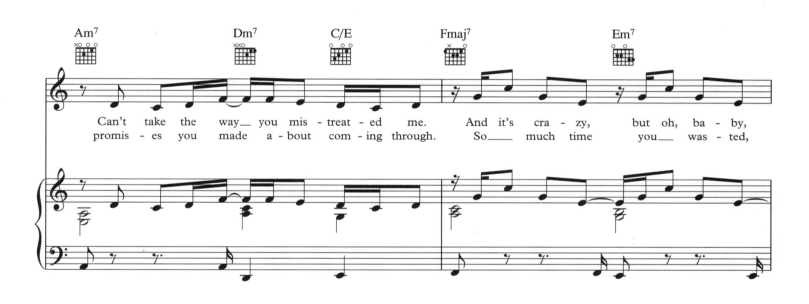

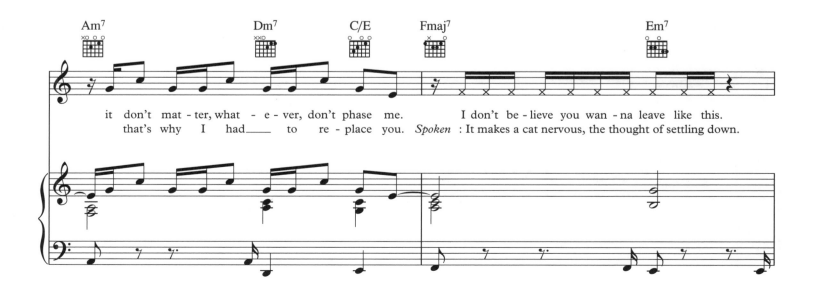

American Life

highest chart position 2
release date 14th April 2003

did you know 'American Life' saw Madonna mutate from the material girl to the military girl – while the khaki-strewn video was controversially withdrawn when the second Gulf War started.

words and music by
Madonna and Mirwais Ahmadzaï

Moderately ♩ = 102

Do I have to change my name? Will it get me far?

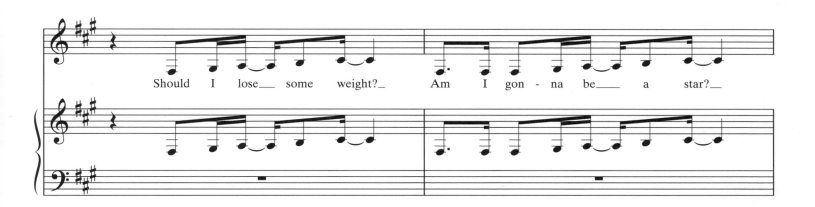

Should I lose some weight? Am I gon-na be a star?

Do I have to change_ my name?_ Am I gon-na be_ a star?_

_ Do I have to change_ my name?_

Repeat ad lib. and fade

Can't Nobody

words and music by

Robert Reed, Tony Fisher and Richard Harrison

highest chart position 5
release date 6th May 2003

did you know Kelendria Rowland is one third of American R&B hit machine Destiny's Child – and she's proved she can hold her own as a solo singer, beginning with US and UK chart-topper, 'Dilemma'. Her success adds spice to frequent comparisons to friend and bandmate Beyoncé, though both deny a rivalry.

1. I'm trying to let you know what it's all a-bout, I know you want to leave.
2. I knew you'd be the one to come out, come out, I need you please to re-

Come Undone

words and music by

**Robert Williams, Daniel Pierre, Ashley Hamilton
and Pierre Ottestad**

highest chart position 4
release date 14th April 2003

did you know Robbie Williams – the multi-millionaire great white hope for EMI, who famously declared "I'm rich beyond my wildest dreams" when signing on the dotted line – here offers advice about the downside of fame. It's the only known song by a former Take That member to include the word 'scum'.

So un-im-pressed but so in awe, such a saint but such a whore.
So rock and roll so cor-porate suit, so damn ug-ly so damn cute.

Couldn't Have Said It Better

words and music by
James Michael and Nikki Sixx

highest chart position **31**
release date **14th April 2003**

did you know **Meat Loaf** recently attempted to promote his new album by singing along to it atop a London double-decker on Oxford Street. Thankfully more pressing street crime meant that his desired arrest by the police never happened.

(Guitar Solo ad lib.)

rall.

Oh_____

This is the mo - ment we've been

Crazy In Love

words and music by

Eugene Record, Beyoncé Knowles, Rich Harrison and Shawn Carter

highest chart position 1
release date 7th July 2003

did you know Nowadays R&B stars rarely confine themselves to just the one medium. Hence Beyoncé has started a film career too, appearing in *The Fighting Temptations* as well as a star turn as Foxxy Cleopatra in *Austin Powers In Goldmember*.

2.

Look-ing so cra-zy, your love's got me look-ing, got me look-ing so cra-zy in love.

I'm warmed up now. Let's go!

Verses 3 & 4 (Jay Z):

3. Young Hov', y'all know when the flow is lo-co. Young B. and the R. O. C., uh oh.
4. *See additional lyrics*

O. G. big hom-ie, the one and on-ly, stick bo-ny, but the pock-et is fat like To-ny

So-pran-o. the ROC han - dle like Van Ex - el I shake phon-ies, man, you can't get next to

Chorus:

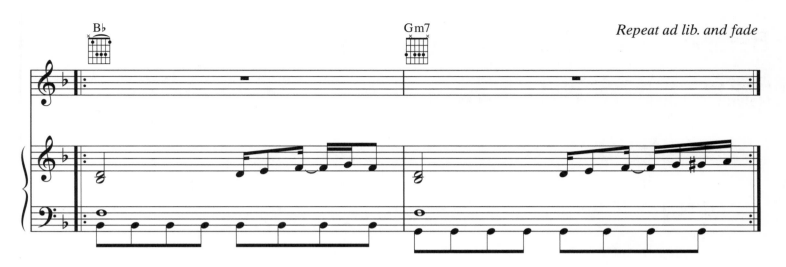

Verse 2:
When I talk to my friends so quietly,
"(Who he think he is?)"
Look at what you've done to me.
Tennis shoes, don't even need to buy a new dress.
If you ain't there, ain't nobody else to impress.
It's the way that you know what I thought I knew.
It's the beat that my heart skips when I'm with you.
But I still don't understand
Just how your love can do what no one else can.
(To Chorus:)

Verse 4:
Jay-Z in the range, crazy and deranged.
They can't figure him out, they're like, "Hey, is he insane?"
Yes, sir, I'm cut from a different cloth.
My texture is the best fur, I'm chinchilla.
I've been ill of the chain smokers.
How you think I got the name Hova?
I've been reala, the game's over.
Fall back, Young.
Ever since I made you change over to platinum,
The game's been a wrap. One!
(To Bridge:)

Here It Comes Again

highest chart position 7
release date 24th February 2003

did you know Apparently our Mel has worked out a time-management technique to keep in shape, both physically and spiritually – she prays and meditates as she jogs. Watch out for those lamp-posts though, lovey.

words and music by
Melanie Chisholm, Marius DeVries and Robert Howard

Hey, don't you wor-ry, ev-'ry-thing's al-right,— you know— we're gon-na be— just— fine. If the rain crash-es down ov-

I Begin To Wonder

words and music by
**Jean-Claude Ades, Olaf Kramolowski
and Dacia Bridges**

highest chart position 2
release date 3rd March 2003

did you know Dannii has recently been brushing up her French skills, appearing in *Notre Dame De Paris*, replacing Tina Arena, whom she knew from their days together in Australia's *Young Talent Time* show. However, her well publicised relationship with Formula One driver Jacques Villeneuve is now over.

1. When I'm walk-ing down the street I call your name, in-side my head I go in-sane.
2. And every time I think I'm break-ing free, these thoughts re-turn to trou-ble me.

Don't you know that it's real-ly mak-ing me cra-zy?
Hang-ing on to love has left me emp-ty.

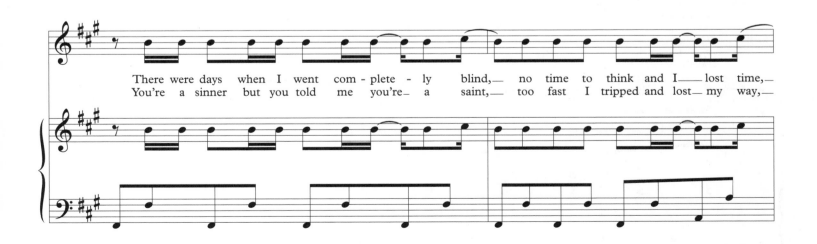

There were days when I went com-plete-ly blind, no time to think and I lost time,
You're a sinner but you told me you're a saint, too fast I tripped and lost my way,

I Can't Break Down

highest chart position 2
release date 10th February 2003

did you know For many the real star to emerge out of the hotch-potch of wannabe pop idol shows, *Fame Academy* runner-up Sinead Quinn won many over with her feisty renditions of Macy Gray's 'I Try' and No Doubt's 'Don't Speak'.

words and music by

Peter Glenister, Sinead Quinn and Deni Lew

Now I know I can han - dle this, I close my mouth and clench my fist. I've lived this day in a thou-sand ways, but there's a flaw to add to my list. Go on

Incredible (What I Meant To Say)

highest chart position 9
release date 3rd March 2003

did you know The shy and retiring graduate of *Pop Stars*, Darius informs us that pretty soon he'll be putting pen to paper to write his autobiography, covering his first three years of fame.

words and music by

Graham Edwards, Scott Spock, Lauren Christy and Darius Danesh

If I Fall

words and music by
Matthew Hales and Kim Oliver

highest chart position **not applicable**
release date **not released at time of publication**
did you know Aqualung recently appeared on the BBC's
Re:covered music show, choosing to play a version of the Beach
Boys' 'God Only Knows', as well as this song.

I'm With You

words and music by

Lauren Christy, David Alspach, Graham Edwards and Avril Lavigne

highest chart position 7
release date 31st March 2003

did you know Descriptions frequently popping up in Lavigne's press kit include 'wild child' and even 'the anti-Britney'. 'Wild child' is even on her official bio. "I'm gonna dress what's me, I'm gonna act what's me and I'm gonna sing what's me," she proudly states. But then 'I'm With You' was a slight change in direction, deploying strings to emphasise her 'introspective' side.

Keep Me A Secret

words and music by

**Ainslie Henderson, Sinead Quinn
and Malachi Cush**

highest chart position 5
release date **24th February 2003**

did you know This song was written whilst the composers were together in the Fame Academy. Ainslie previously endeared himself to the show's fans (not least the 'headmaster') with his left-field take on the Pretenders' 'Don't Get Me Wrong'.

I'm tryin' not to feel you but— you've just brushed by,— and if you dare to cross— that line— you know— my toes would step on fire,— oh,—

Lost Without You

words by **Bridget Benenate**   *music by* **Matthew Gerrard**

highest chart position 4
release date **23rd June 2003**

did you know A former star of Australian soap opera, Delta has endured endless and inevitable comparisons with the Minogue sisters. This is the follow-up to her debut hit 'Born To Try'.

I know I can be a lit-tle stub-born some-times

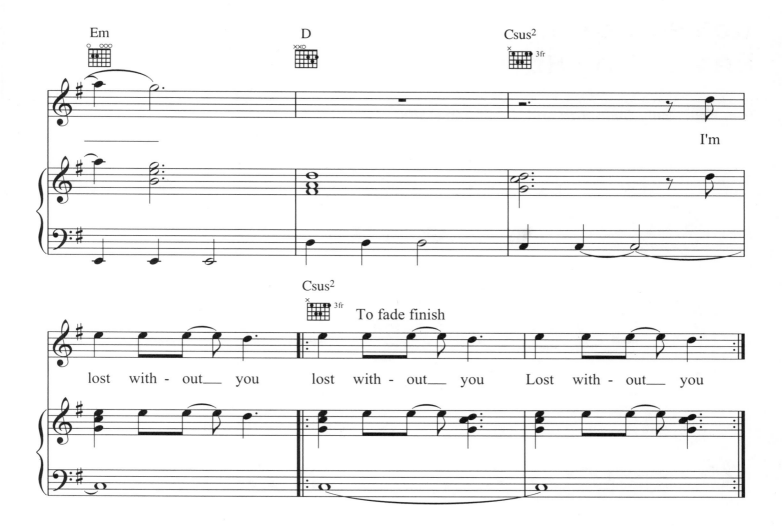

Em   D   Csus²

I'm

Csus²

To fade finish

lost with - out__ you   lost with - out__ you   Lost with - out__ you

How my ever gonna get rid of these blues
Baby I'm so lonely all the time
Everywhere I go I get so confused
You're the only thing that's on my mind

Oh my beds so cold at night and I miss you more each day
Only you can make it right no I'm not too proud to say

All I know is I'm lost without you I'm not gonna lie
How my going to be strong without you I need you by my side
If we ever say we'll never be together and we ended with goodbye
don't know what I'd do....I'm lost without you
I keep trying to find my way but all I know is I'm lost without you
I keep trying to face the day I'm lost without you

If I could only hold you now and make the pain just go away
Can't stop the tears from running down my face
Oh

All I know is I'm lost without you I'm not gonna lie
How my going to be strong without you I need you by my side
If we ever say we'll never be together and we ended with goodbye
don't know what I'd do....I'm lost without you

I keep trying to find my way but all I know is I'm lost without you
I keep trying to face the day I'm lost without you

Love Doesn't Have To Hurt

words and music by

Tom Kelly, Billy Steinberg and Susannah Hoffs

highest chart position 4
release date 31st March 2003
did you know Atomic Kitten have just been nominated for Best Group in the Disney Channel Kids Awards, while 'It's OK' was voted record of the year by listeners to Heart FM. At the latter awards Lil bid in the charity auction in aid of Nordoff Robbins – securing a holiday in France for her mum.

I learnt a les - son in my life,____ but I learnt it the hard— way.—

I don't know why I used to fall in love____ with the wrong—

Make Me Smile (Come Up And See Me)

highest chart position **14**
release date **7th April 2003**
did you know **Erasure have always been fond of their covers, especially the Abba-esque EP. Here they turn to those other mainstays of the 70s airwaves, Steve Harley and Cockney Rebel.**

words and music by
Steve Harley

107

Midnight

words and music by

Charlotte Gordon, Jenna Gibbons, Iyiola Babalola, Darren Lewis, Jim Morrison, John Densmore, Robert Krieger and Raymond Manzarek

highest chart position **26**
release date **17th March 2003**

did you know Un-cut, the next big thing in drum and bass and breakbeat music, were originally known as Future Cut. The voice belongs to Jenna G, who was headhunted for the band after Darren (Lewis) saw her in hip hop outfit Subliminal Darkness.

1. Can't wait— 'til this day is ov- er, can't wait— for this day to be— done.
2. Can't get— up, I must come down, can't get— the bells to stop ring-ing.

No Good Advice

highest chart position 2
release date 19th May 2003

did you know Before the release of this single, singer Cheryl Tweedy was involved in a fracas at a Guildford nightclub and charged with racially aggravated assault. She was accused of attacking toilet attendant Sophie Amogbokpa at the Drink nightspot.

words and music by
Miranda Cooper, Brian Higgins, Timothy Powell, Matthew Gray, Lisa Cowling, Nick Coler, Shawn Mahan, Tim Larcombe and Lene Nystrom

1. Dad - dy told me look___ in - to the fu - ture, sit___ at your com - pu - ter, be___ a good girl.

2. Dad - dy al - ways told___ me to re - mem - ber leave___ the boys 'til lat - er, don't___ you drop down.

Ma - ma said re - mem - ber you're a la - dy, think___

Ma - ma said I'd nev - er get to heav - en hang -

Not Gonna Get Us

highest chart position 7
release date 27th May 2003

did you know In a recent edition of *Word*, Morrissey was asked about the duo's version of The Smiths' 'How Soon Is Now'.
Word: Did you hear t.A.T.u.'s version of 'How Soon Is Now'?
Morrissey: Yes, it was magnificent. Absolutely. Again, I don't know much about them. *Word*: They are teenage Russian lesbians.
Morrissey: Well, aren't we all?

words and music by
**Trevor Horn, Elena Kiper, Ivan Shapovalov,
Sergej Galoyan and Valerij Polienko**

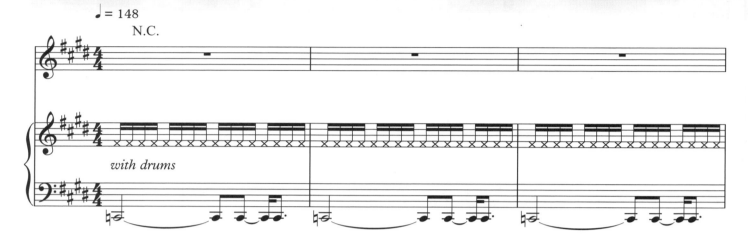

Say Goodbye

words and music by
Christopher Braide and Cathy Dennis

highest chart position 2
release date **2nd June 2003**

did you know This is the final farewell single from the group that launched more factions than *Pop Idols* and *Fame Academy* combined. Needless to say, fans can look forward to myriad solo careers.

1. In the years to come, will you think a-bout these mo-ments that we shared?

(2.) year from now, May-be there'll be things we'll wish we nev-er said.

In the years to come are you gon-na think it o-ver? And

In a year from now, may-be we'll see each oth-er

On The Horizon

words and music by
**Gregg Alexander, Rick Nowels
and Melanie Chisholm**

highest chart position 14
release date 9th June 2003

did you know The former members of the Spice Girls, including Mel C, got together in February 2003 for a 'chat'. Rumours were rife in the British tabloids that they'd decided to reunite due to fading solo fortunes. But nothing concrete has emerged, and Mel C's career has been going far better than most of her former colleagues.

Peo - ple see dif - fe - rent things —— when — they — look —— on the ho - ri -

Out Of Time

highest chart position 5
release date 14th April 2003
did you know If you visit Blur's website you can download the Crazy Beat game for free – the boys' very own tribute to retro gaming.

words by
Damon Albarn

music by
Damon Albarn, Alex James and David Rowntree

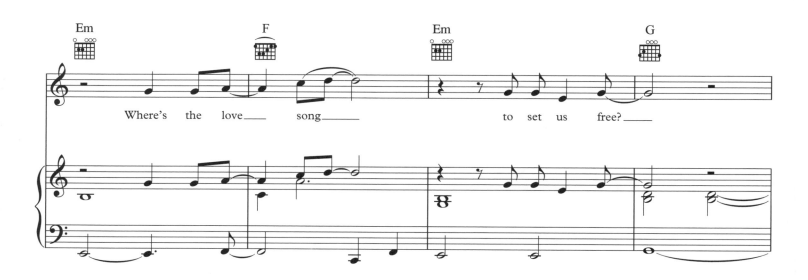

Where's the love___ song___ to set us free?___

Too man-y peo-ple___ down,___ ev'-ry-thing turn-ing___ the wrong___

Instrumental Solo ad lib.

Rock Your Body

words and music by
**Chad Hugo, Pharrell Williams
and Justin Timberlake**

highest chart position 2
release date 27th May 2003

did you know Timberlake, the babe magnet, who once dated Britney et al, reaches his zenith as a lover with this song's Barry White-esque line, "Better have you naked by the end of this song". Lovers of romance can opt for the extended remix, presumably.

Bridge:

have you nak-ed by the end of this song. So what did you come

_ for when you know that you_ don't_ wan - na hit
(I came_ to dance with you._)

the door. You've been search - ing for_ love for - ev -
(Here to_ ro - mance with you._) (Ba - by,

N.C.

Repeat ad lib. and fade

Verse 2:
I don't mean no harm,
Just wanna rock you, girl.
You can move but be calm.
Let's go, let's give it a whirl.
See, it appears to me
You like the way I move.
I'll tell you what I'm gonna do,
Pull you close and share my groove.
(To Pre-chorus:)

Spirit In The Sky

words and music by
Norman Greenbaum

highest chart position 1
release date 10th March 2003

did you know Gates chooses to return to Norman Greenbaum's song, which made him a one-hit wonder (and later was taken to No.1 by Dr And The Medics, who were also cursed with the same tag). Luckily he's already had some hits, so the 'curse' won't rub off on him.

1. When I die and they lay me to rest,__ Gon-na go to the place__that's the best.__

Sunday (The Day Before My Birthday)

words and music by
Moby and Sylvia Robinson

highest chart position **did not chart**
release date **3rd March 2003**
did you know Although a mild-mannered vegan type,
Moby seems to have incurred the wrath of Eminem,
who recently took to decapitating a model of him on stage
while on tour. Apparently Moby said something about him
not respecting women in his lyrics…

Sunrise

words and music by

**Daryl Hall, John Oates, Sara Allen
and Mick Hucknall**

highest chart position 7
release date **17th March 2003**

did you know Most of the members of venerable white soul warblers Simply Red actually came together in the punk days as The Frantic Elevators. In fact, Mick Hucknall was even sighted at The Sex Pistols' first gig in Manchester.

Thinking About Tomorrow

words and music by

**Ted Barnes, Beth Orton, Sean Read
and Sebastian Steinberg**

highest chart position **57**
release date **31st March 2003**
did you know **Prior to the release of her own material, Orton guested on material by The Chemical Brothers and William Orbit, who produced her debut album. She also used another dance music guru, Andy Weatherall, on the second. This is taken from 'Daybreaker', featuring Ben Watt of Everything But The Girl as her musical collaborator.**

1. Tired but I ain't sleep-ing. Think-ing a-bout some sad af-fair.
2. Tired but I ain't dream-ing. Fall-ing in-to so-lid air.

And why I should be leav-ing. 'Cause
And why I must be leav-ing. 'Cause

some of these thoughts___ on - ly seem to take___ me out___ of here.___ Yeah,__ these
one of these days___ I'm gon - na pull___ out all___ my hair.__

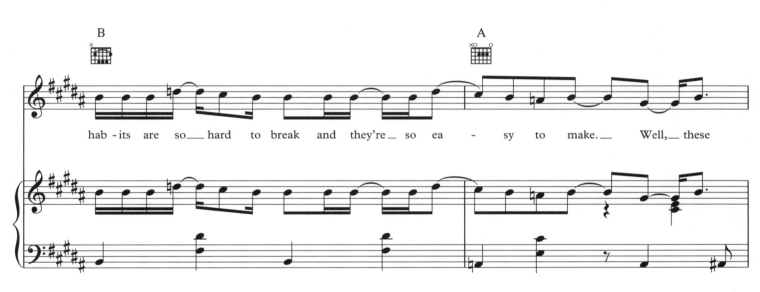

hab -its are so___ hard to break and they're__ so ea - sy to make.__ Well,__ these

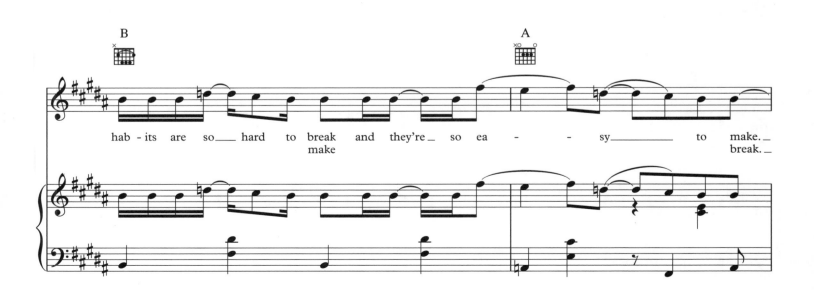

hab -its are so___ hard to break and they're__ so ea - - sy___ to make.__
make
break.__

To Love A Woman

words and music by
Lionel Richie, Paul Barry and Enrique Iglesias

highest chart position 19
release date 14th April 2003

did you know A collaboration between one of the late 70s/early 80s most successful soul artists and the heir to father Julio's blue-eyed Latin soul tradition. If their collective fan-bases jumped up and down at exactly the same time there would be a tidal wave in Hawaii.

I don't know what it is but she drives me cra - zy,

I don't know what she does but she drives me wild.

If on - ly she could let me be —— the man —— I want to be,

Wimmin

words and music by
**Ashley Hamilton, Christopher Lloyd
and Robert Williams**

highest chart position **27**
release date **9th June 2003**

did you know Hamilton has not one, but two famous fathers (Rod Stewart biologically, and actor George Hamilton is his stepfather). He'd already been through the celebrity treadmill before launching a musical career, and this effort was co-written by friend Robbie Williams.

You Said No

words and music by
John McLaughlin, Stephen Robson, James Bourne, Matthew Sargeant, Charles Simpson and Richard Rashman

highest chart position 1
release date 28th April 2003
did you know Charlie, Mattie and James, the skate punk boys from next door, won many female hearts with this honest appraisal of male failure in the art of courtship and procuring a girlfriend.

You're so fit___ and you know it, and I on-ly dream___ of___ you. 'Cause my life's___ such a bitch,___

YOU'RE THE VOICE

Maria Callas

8861A PV/CD
Casta Diva from Norma – Vissi D'arte from Tosca – Un Bel Di Vedremo from Madama Butterfly – Addio, Del Passato from La Traviata – J'ai Perdu Mon Eurydice from Orphee Et Eurydice – Les Tringles Des Sistres Tintaient from Carmen – Porgi Amor from Le Nozze Di Figaro – Ave Maria from Otello

Tom Jones

8860A PVG/CD
Delilah – Green Green Grass Of Home – Help Yourself – I'll Never Fall In Love Again – It's Not Unusual – Mama Told Me Not To Come – Sexbomb – Thunderball – What's New Pussycat – You Can Leave Your Hat On

Celine Dion

9297A PVG/CD
Beauty And The Beast – Because You Loved Me – Falling Into You – The First Time Ever I Saw Your Face – It's All Coming Back To Me Now – Misled – My Heart Will Go On – The Power Of Love – Think Twice – When I Fall In Love

ARETHA FRANKLIN

9349A PVG/CD
Chain Of Fools – A Deeper Love Do Right Woman, Do Right Man – I Knew You Were Waiting (For Me) – I Never Loved A Man (The Way I Loved You) – I Say A Little Prayer – Respect – Think – Who's Zooming Who – (You Make Me Feel Like) A Natural Woman

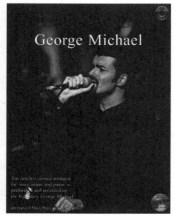

George Michael

9007A PVG/CD
Careless Whisper – A Different Corner – Faith – Father Figure – Freedom '90 – I'm Your Man – I Knew You Were Waiting (For Me) – Jesus To A Child – Older – Outside

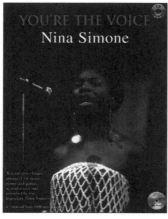

Nina Simone

9606A PVG/CD
Don't Let Me Be Misunderstood – Feeling Good – I Loves You Porgy – I Put A Spell On You – Love Me Or Leave Me – Mood Indigo – My Baby Just Cares For Me – Ne Me Quitte Pas (If You Go Away) – Nobody Knows You When You're Down And Out – Take Me To The Water

Carole King

9700A PVG/CD
Beautiful – Crying In The Rain – I Feel The Earth Move – It's Too Late – (You Make Me Feel Like) A Natural Woman – So Far Away – Way Over Yonder – Where You Lead – Will You Love Me Tomorrow – You've Got A Friend

Frank Sinatra

9746A PVG/CD
April In Paris – Come Rain Or Come Shine – Fly Me To The Moon (In Other Words) – I've Got You Under My Skin – The Lady Is A Tramp – My Kinda Town (Chicago Is) – My Way – Theme From *New York, New York* – Someone To Watch Over Me – Something Stupid

Barbra Streisand

9770A PVG/CD
Cry Me A River – Evergreen (A Star Is Born) – Happy Days Are Here Again – I've Dreamed Of You – Memory – My Heart Belongs To Me – On A Clear Day (You Can See Forever) – Someday My Prince Will Come – Tell Him (duet with Celine Dion) – The Way We Were

Bette Midler

9799A PVG/CD
Boogie Woogie Bugle Boy – Chapel Of Love – Friends – From A Distance – Hello In There – One For My Baby (And One More For The Road) – Only In Miami – The Rose – When A Man Loves A Woman – Wind Beneath My Wings

Eva Cassidy

9810A PVG/CD
Ain't No Sunshine – Autumn Leaves – How Can I Keep From Singing – Imagine – It Doesn't Matter Anymore – Over The Rainbow – Penny To My Name – People Get Ready – Wayfaring Stranger – What A Wonderful World

Matt Monro

9889A PVG/CD
Around The World – Born Free – From Russia With Love – Gonna Build A Mountain – The Impossible Dream – My Kind Of Girl – On A Clear Day You Can See Forever – Portrait Of My Love – Softly As I Leave You – Walk Away

The outstanding vocal series from IMP

CD contains full backings for each song, professionally arranged to recreate the sounds of the original recording